# CUT & PASTE SIGHT WORD SENTENCES

## Written by

Barbara Maio and Rozanne Lanczak Williams

**Editor**: Dorothy Ly
**Designer/Production**: Karen Nguyen
**Art Director**: Moonhee Pak
**Project Director**: Stacey Faulkner

# Table of Contents

## CUT & PASTE SIGHT WORD REPRODUCIBLES

# Introduction

Sight words are those words beginning readers should instantly recognize. They are among a group of high frequency words that compose up to 75% of the words that children encounter in text and use in their own writing on a daily basis. Many of these sight words do not follow standard phonics rules or spelling patterns, which makes them difficult for early readers to recognize and sound out. For beginning readers, automatic recognition of sight words helps build both fluency and comprehension. Therefore, it is important for beginning readers to practice their sight words until they can read them quickly and fluently. Current research supports practicing sight words in the context of phrases and short sentences.

*Cut & Paste Sight Word Sentences* provides beginning readers with a unique, hands-on approach to help them master over 100 common high frequency words while building and strengthening higher level comprehension skills. When children are starting to read, the text rarely provides opportunities for developing comprehension skills beyond basic recall. As students discuss how they will complete the picture part of each sentence reproducible, they tap into higher levels of comprehension and think outside the box in creative and imaginative ways!

## 10 Top Skills Developed with Cut & Paste Sight Word Sentences

- Concepts of print (left to right directionality; what makes a word; words make a sentence)
- Sight word recognition
- Vocabulary development
- Parts of speech
- Sentence structure
- Types of sentences (telling, asking, exclamatory)
- Punctuation
- Prewriting skills
- Comprehension (literal and higher level)
- Following directions

have | picnic. | will | a | *We

*We | will | have | a | picnic.

We will have a picnic.

# Using the Cut & Paste Sight Word Sentences

Sentence pages do not have to be used in any particular order. First, select the sentence page you want to use with your students, or to focus on specific sight words, refer to the chart on pages 6–7. Then follow the directed lesson format steps below.

**1.** Working with a small group, give each student a reproducible sentence page. Have students point to the words (moving from left to right) as you read each one. Repeat this several times, until students "get" the words and can read them automatically. Then ask *each* student to read *every* word independently.

**2.** Help students identify the beginning word of the sentence—the word with the capital letter and marked with an asterisk. As the children progress, they will learn that the first word always starts with a capital letter.

**3.** Help students find the last word in the sentence—the word with punctuation (. ? !).

**4.** Guide students to practice reading and pointing to the words in correct sentence order. For example, with the sentence "I like this," cue them by saying, *I _____ this*. Have students point to the word that fits in the blank (like). Then ask them to point and read all the words several times in correct sentence order.

**5.** Ask each student, one at a time, to read and point to the words in the correct sentence order.

**6.** Next, focus on the (incomplete) illustration. Build vocabulary by discussing what could be in the picture. Generate, and encourage, a variety of ideas that are higher level, creative and imaginative. For example, with the sentence "I like this," ask students what

"I" means (who and how many people will be in the picture) and what "this" means (an object, activity, event, or place). Or when illustrating the sentence "Come see my bugs," illustrations should have at least 2 bugs (since "bugs" is plural).

**7.** After students practice the words and sentences and discuss the illustrations, focus attention on the 5 icons at the top of each page — 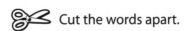 — and instruct students to follow the order of the icons as they complete the page.

 Cut the words apart.

| see | my | bugs. | *Come |
|-----|-----|-------|-------|

✓ Arrange the words in correct sentence order on the page. No gluing yet! The teacher, parent helper, aide, or reliable student needs to check that the words are in the correct order before gluing.

| *Come | see | my | bugs. |
|-------|-----|-----|-------|

 Glue the sentence words in the blank space beside the glue bottle icon.

Copy the sentence on the writing line under the pencil icon.

 Complete the illustration by drawing and coloring a picture that matches the sentence and shows comprehension of the text.

8. Have students complete their work independently as you call up another group and repeat the lesson. As a follow-up activity, invite students to share their artwork and explain their thinking.

9. Have students place their completed sentence pages in folders. Then after a number of pages have been completed, show students how to staple them to the cover on page 8 to make a book. To connect school to home, send the books home once a week so students can practice reading the sentences and share their work with family members.

10. Save samples to show parents their child's remarkable progress in printing, small motor development, divergent thinking, and reading comprehension!

## Home-School Connection

### Sight Word Phrases

On page 59, there are 60 phrases using the same sight words found in the sentence pages. Use this page as an assessment tool for each student by recording each phrase mastered. This page can also be cut apart and sent home to give students extra practice.

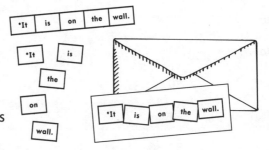

### Sight Word Sentence Strips

On pages 60–64, the sight word sentences are in sentence strip format. After completing a few of the reproducible sentence pages, send the corresponding sentence strips home. Have students cut the words apart, form the sentences and practice reading them. Cut-apart sentences can be stored in envelopes for future at-home practice.

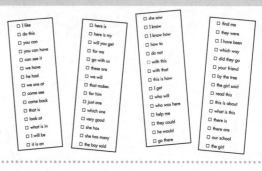

# Sight Word Reference Chart

Here is a handy chart that will help you plan your instruction. It lists the featured sight words in alphabetical order and on what sentence pages they appear.

| SIGHT WORDS | CUT & PASTE SENTENCE PAGE | SIGHT WORDS | CUT & PASTE SENTENCE PAGE |
|---|---|---|---|
| a | 21, 39, 55 | found | 43 |
| about | 58 | friend | 22 |
| again | 49 | from | 40 |
| all | 30 | get | 32, 36, 50 |
| and | 19, 29 | girl | 57 |
| are | 16, 40 | give | 55 |
| at | 16, 47 | go | 28, 49, 53 |
| back | 18 | good | 35 |
| be | 23, 24 | had | 39 |
| been | 52 | has | 37 |
| before | 52 | have | 13,  21, 45, 52 |
| big | 19 | he | 39 |
| book | 58 | help | 48 |
| box | 25 | her | 31 |
| boy | 38 | here | 18, 20, 22, 26, 27, 30, 35, 52 |
| by | 15 | him | 32 |
| can | 11, 13, 14, 23, 26, 28, 33 | his | 26 |
| come | 17, 18 | home | 55 |
| could | 48, 55 | house | 56 |
| did | 53 | how | 41, 50 |
| do | 10, 41, 42 | I | 9, 11, 23, 41, 44, 49, 50, 52, 54 |
| down | 38 | in | 25 |
| eat | 30 | is | 12, 15, 19, 22, 25, 34, 35, 46, 50, 58 |
| find | 14 | it | 11, 12, 15, 29, 32, 54 |
| for | 32, 36 | just | 33 |

Cut & Paste Sight Word Sentences • Gr. K–1 © 2012 Creative Teaching Press

| SIGHT WORDS | CUT & PASTE SENTENCE PAGE | SIGHT WORDS | CUT & PASTE SENTENCE PAGE |
|---|---|---|---|
| know | 41 | the | 12, 15, 25, 38, 54, 56, 57, 58 |
| like | 9, 10, 27 | their | 35 |
| little | 37 | them | 55 |
| look | 43, 47 | there | 44, 49 |
| makes | 31 | these | 40 |
| many | 37 | they | 43, 51, 53 |
| me | 14, 36, 40, 48 | this | 9, 10, 13, 24, 36, 48, 50, 57 |
| my | 17, 22 | to | 10, 27, 40, 41, 44, 50 |
| new | 45, 47 | tree | 15 |
| not | 42 | two | 56 |
| of | 39 | under | 54 |
| on | 12 | us | 28 |
| one | 33, 34 | very | 51 |
| our | 47 | want | 44 |
| outside | 56 | was | 20 |
| play | 27, 42 | way | 53 |
| put | 38, 54 | we | 10, 16, 21, 27, 30, 45 |
| ran | 29 | were | 51, 56 |
| read | 57 | what | 23, 24, 25, 43, 46, 58 |
| red | 19 | which | 34, 53 |
| run | 26 | who | 20, 48, 55 |
| said | 38, 57 | will | 21, 24, 30, 32, 36 |
| saw | 29 | wish | 46 |
| school | 16, 50 | with | 28, 42, 48 |
| see | 11, 17 | work | 35 |
| she | 29, 37 | would | 49 |
| so | 31 | you | 13, 14, 28, 32, 33, 36, 40 |
| take | 33 | your/yours | 34, 46 |
| that | 19, 31, 38, 41, 42 | | |

# 's

# Sight Word

## Sentences Book

this.

*I

like

**We** | **do** | **this.** | **like** | **to**

Cut & Paste Sight Word Sentences • Gr. K–1 © 2012 Creative Teaching Press

*I    see    can    it.

is    wall.    on    *It    the

Cut & Paste Sight Word Sentences • Gr. K–1 © 2012 Creative Teaching Press

have     can     this.     *You

Cut & Paste Sight Word Sentences • Gr. K-1 © 2012 Creative Teaching Press

14

*Can

you

find

me?

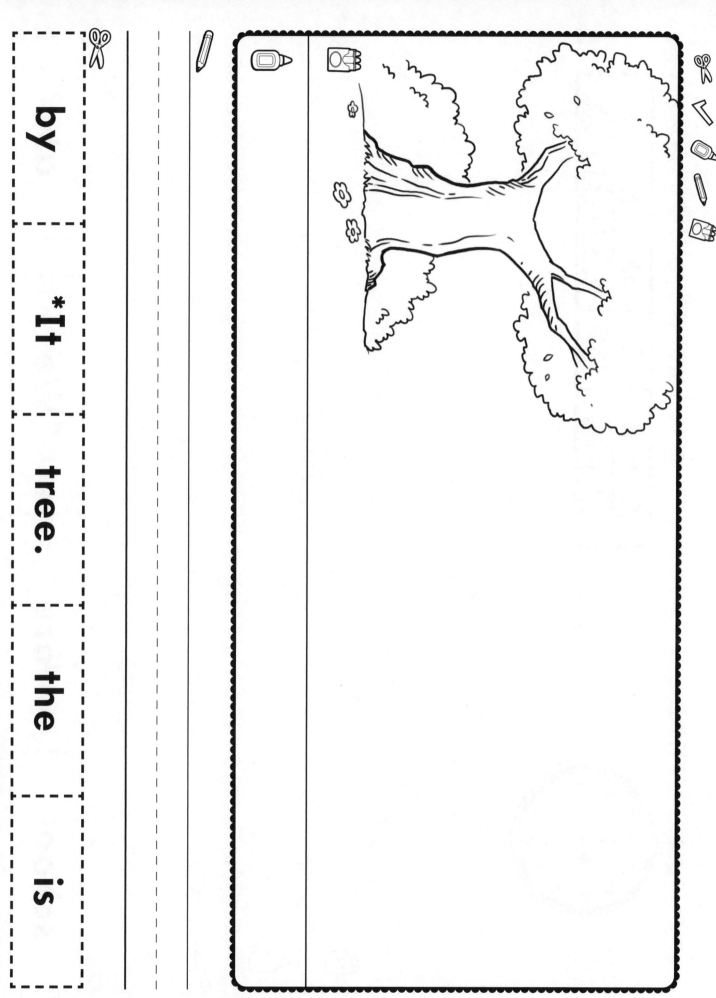

by

*It

tree.

the

is

| A | B | C | D | E | F |
|---|---|---|---|---|---|
| | | | | | |

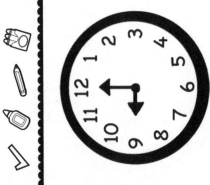

**school.**

**are**

**\*We**

**at**

Cut & Paste Sight Word Sentences • Gr. K–1 © 2012 Creative Teaching Press

my see bugs.

*Come

*Come

back

here!

Cut & Paste Sight Word Sentences • Gr. K–1 © 2012 Creative Teaching Press

is | red. | *That | and | big

Cut & Paste Sight Word Sentences • Gr. K–1 © 2012 Creative Teaching Press

was　　*Who　　here?

Cut & Paste Sight Word Sentences • Gr. K–1 © 2012 Creative Teaching Press

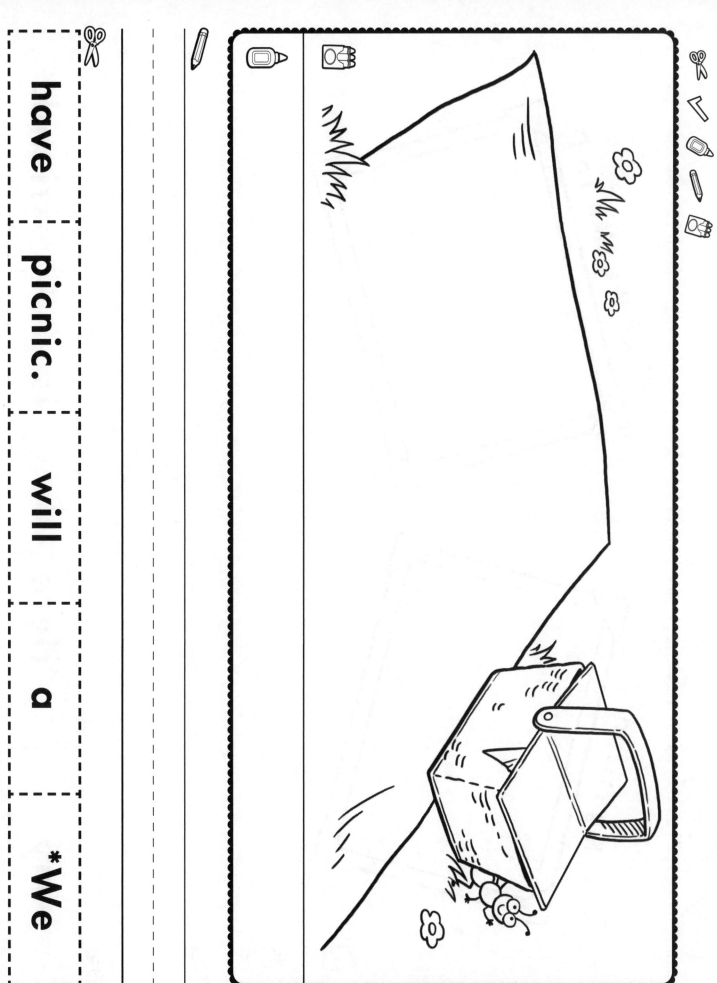

have | picnic. | will | a | *We

Cut & Paste Sight Word Sentences • Gr. K–1 © 2012 Creative Teaching Press

What We Like To Do

My Friend

my   *Here   is   friend.

Cut & Paste Sight Word Sentences • Gr. K–1 © 2012 Creative Teaching Press

I

*What

be?

can

this    *What    will    be?

Cut & Paste Sight Word Sentences • Gr. K–1 © 2012 Creative Teaching Press

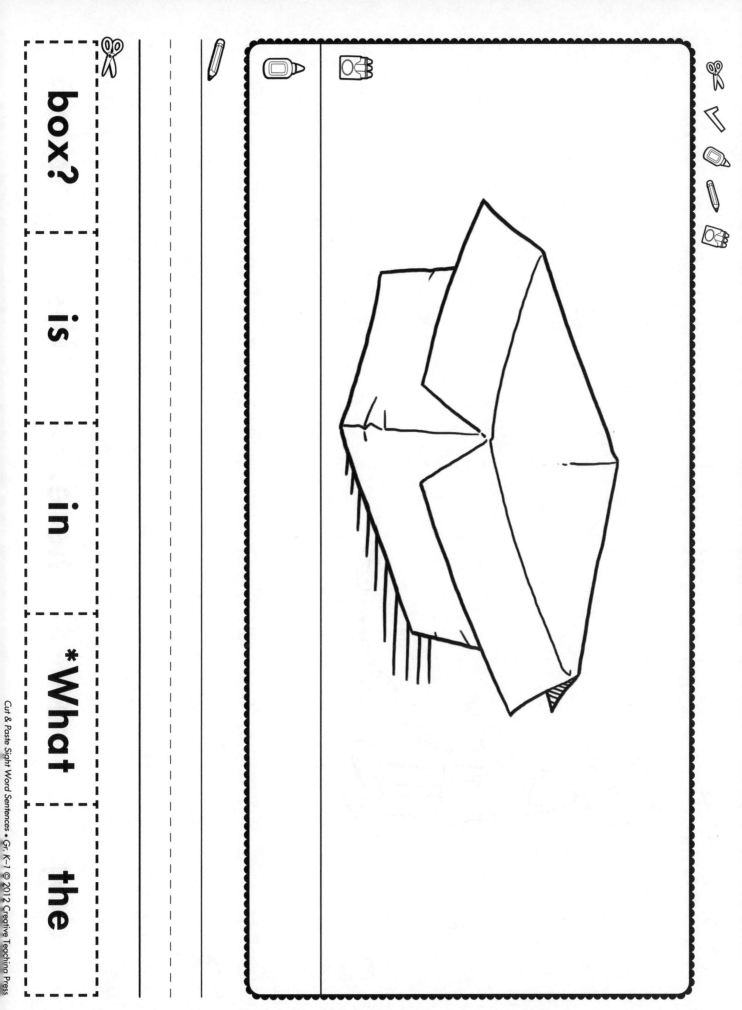

box?   is   in   *What   the

Cut & Paste Sight Word Sentences • Gr. K–1 © 2012 Creative Teaching Press

dog | run | here. | *His | can

Cut & Paste Sight Word Sentences • Gr. K–1 © 2012 Creative Teaching Press

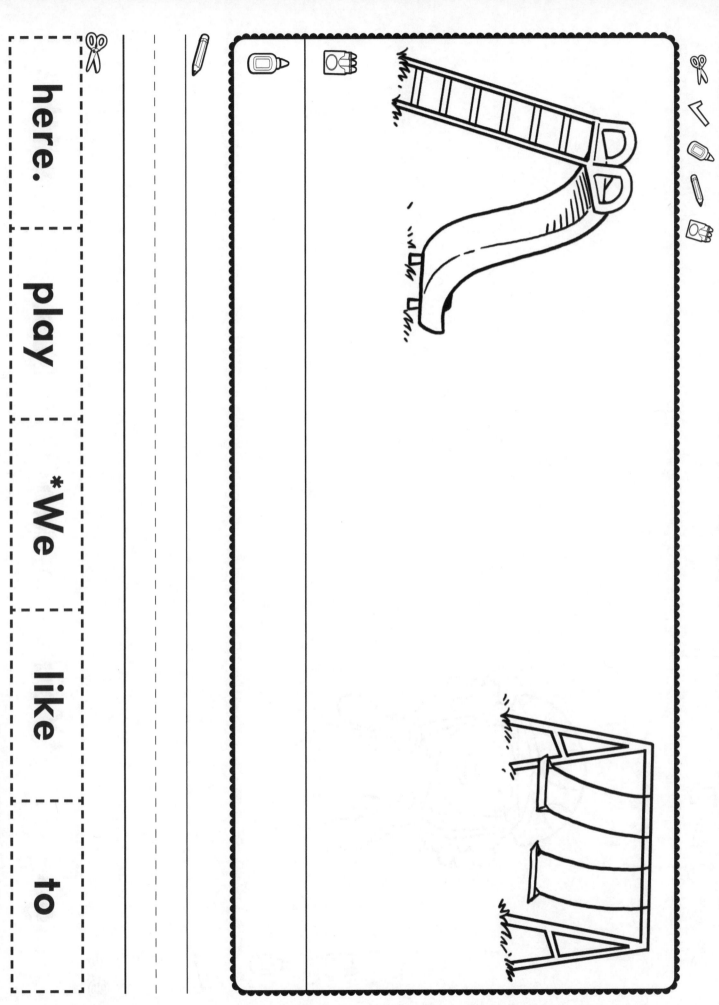

here.

play

*We

like

to

go    *You    can    us.    with

ran.

it

saw

*She

and

Cut & Paste Sight Word Sentences • Gr. K–1 © 2012 Creative Teaching Press

eat   will   *We   here.   all

makes | *That | her | so | happy!

get | it | *Will | you | for | him?

Cut & Paste Sight Word Sentences • Gr. K–1 © 2012 Creative Teaching Press

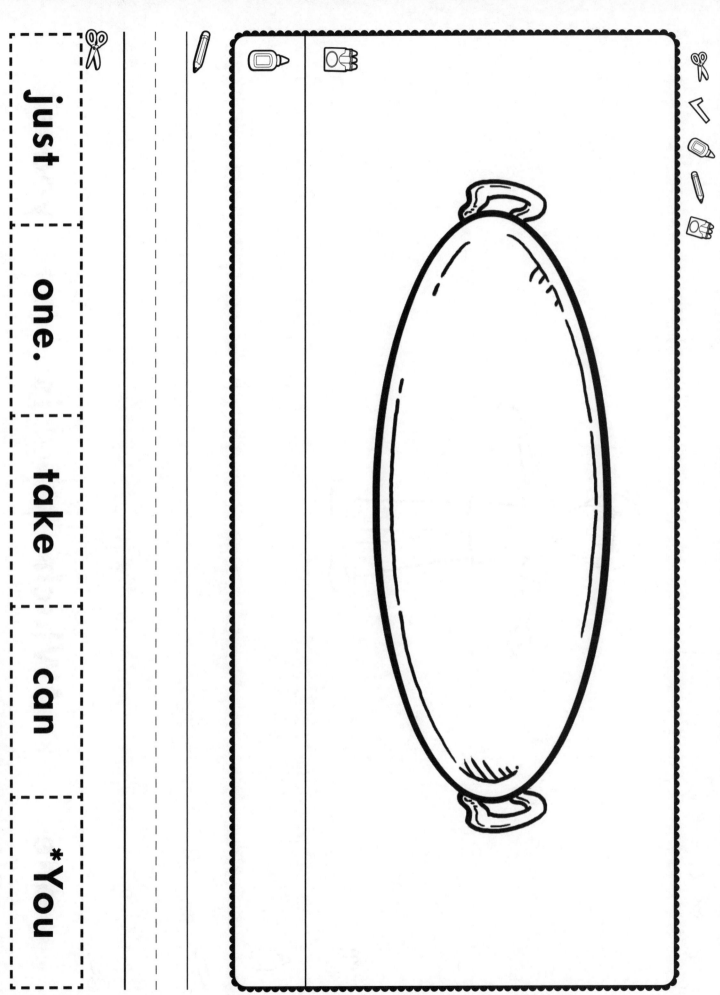

just | one. | take | can | *You

Cut & Paste Sight Word Sentences • Gr. K–1 © 2012 Creative Teaching Press

one *Which is yours?

# Good Work!

| work. | their | good | is | *Here |
|-------|-------|------|----|----|

Cut & Paste Sight Word Sentences • Gr. K–1 © 2012 Creative Teaching Press

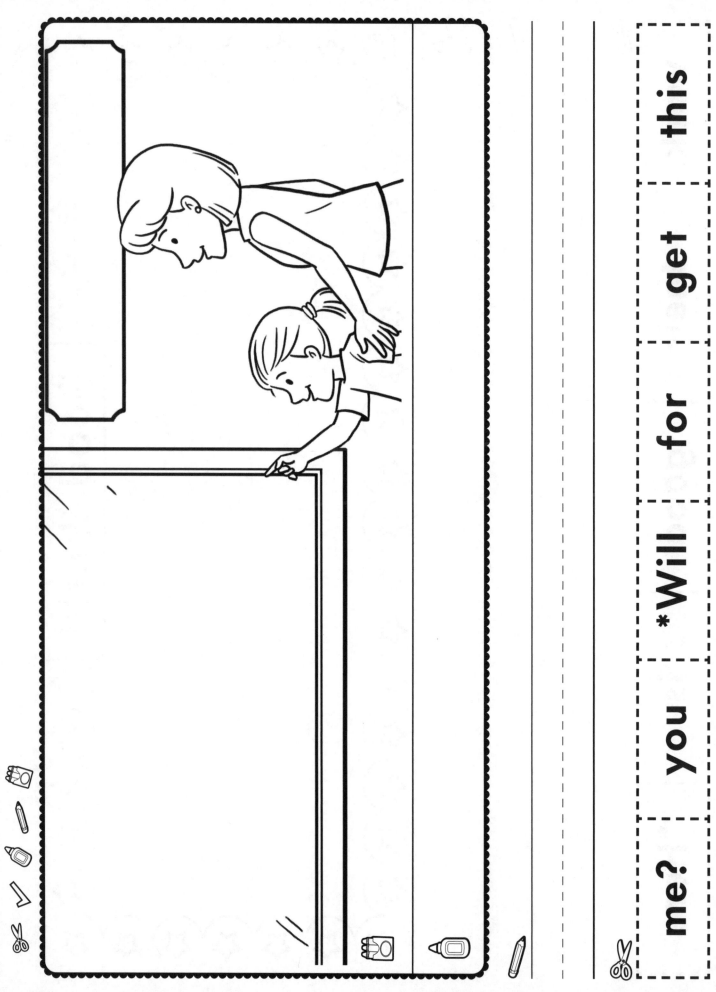

me? | you | *Will | for | get | this

Cut & Paste Sight Word Sentences • Gr. K–1 © 2012 Creative Teaching Press

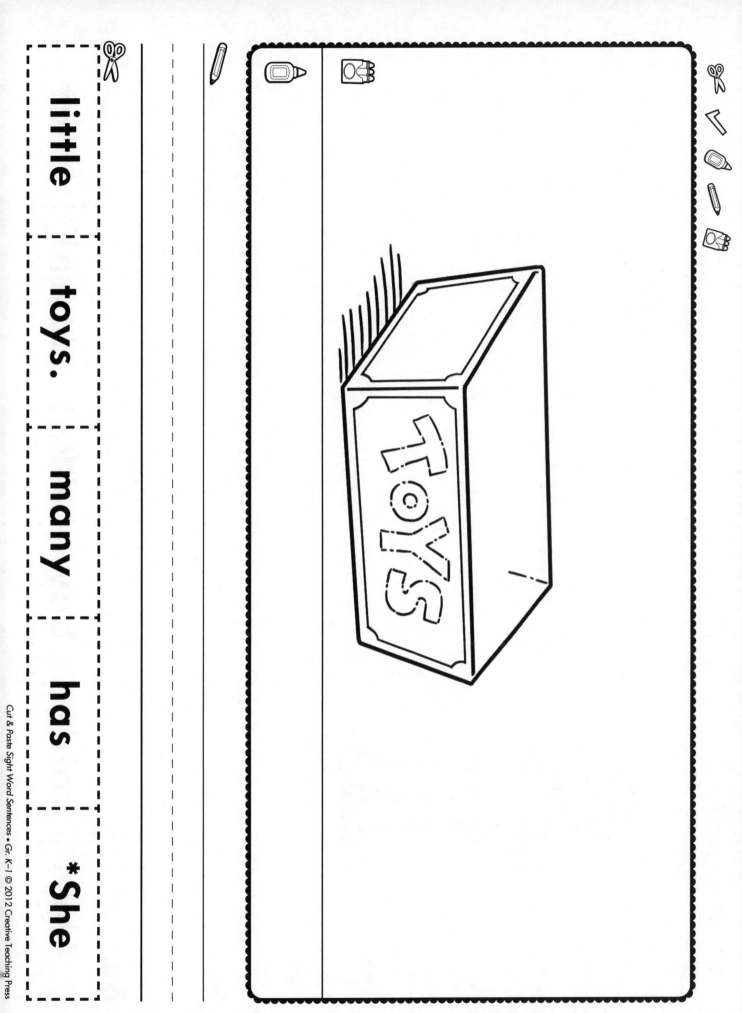

little | toys. | many | has | *She

The | said, | boy | "Put | down!" | that

Cut & Paste Sight Word Sentences • Gr. K–1 © 2012 Creative Teaching Press

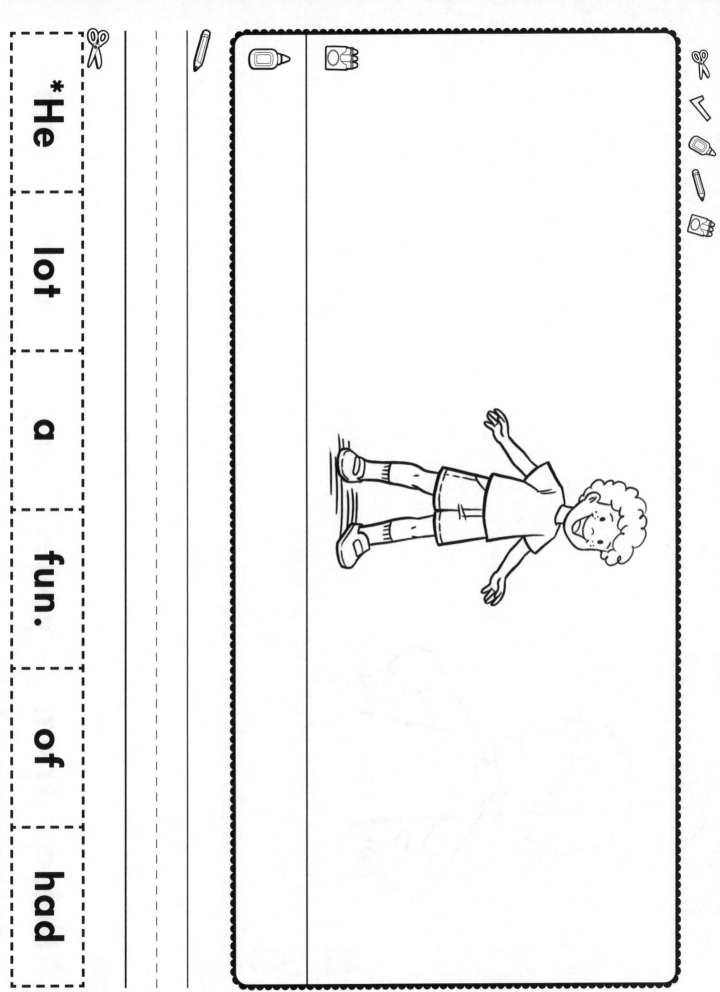

Cut & Paste Sight Word Sentences • Gr. K–1 © 2012 Creative Teaching Press

*He

lot

a

fun.

of

had

*These from you. to are me

How to _____

FIRST

NEXT

LAST

.

know    *I    how    that.    do    to

with

not

play

*Do

that!

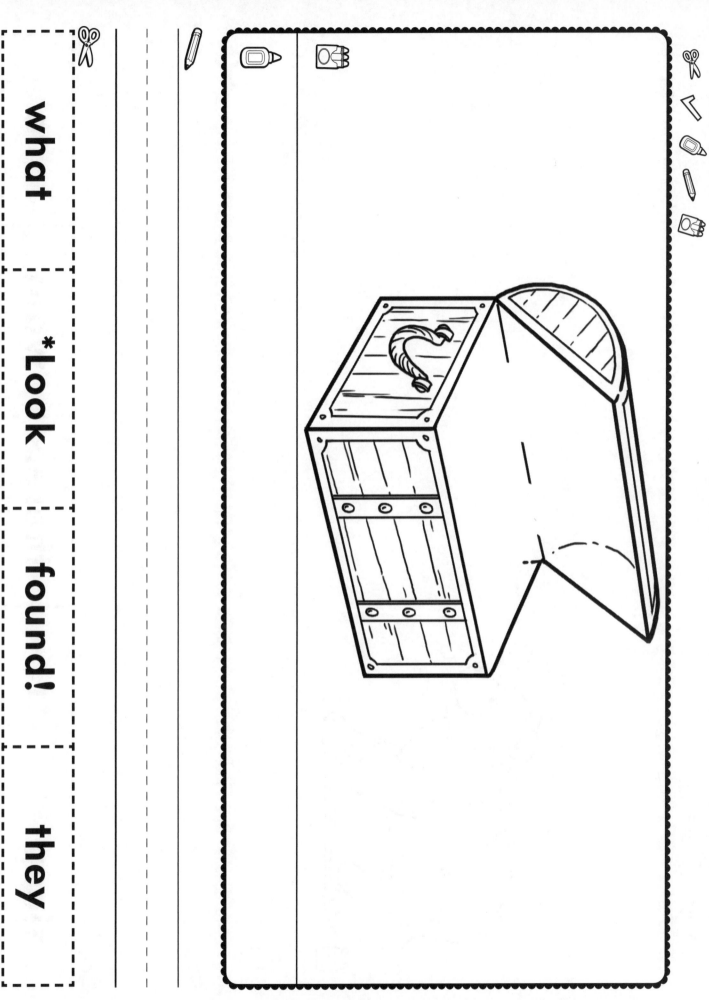

what | *Look | found! | they

Cut & Paste Sight Word Sentences • Gr. K–1 © 2012 Creative Teaching Press

sleep   *I   there.   want   to

Cut & Paste Sight Word Sentences • Gr. K–1 © 2012 Creative Teaching Press

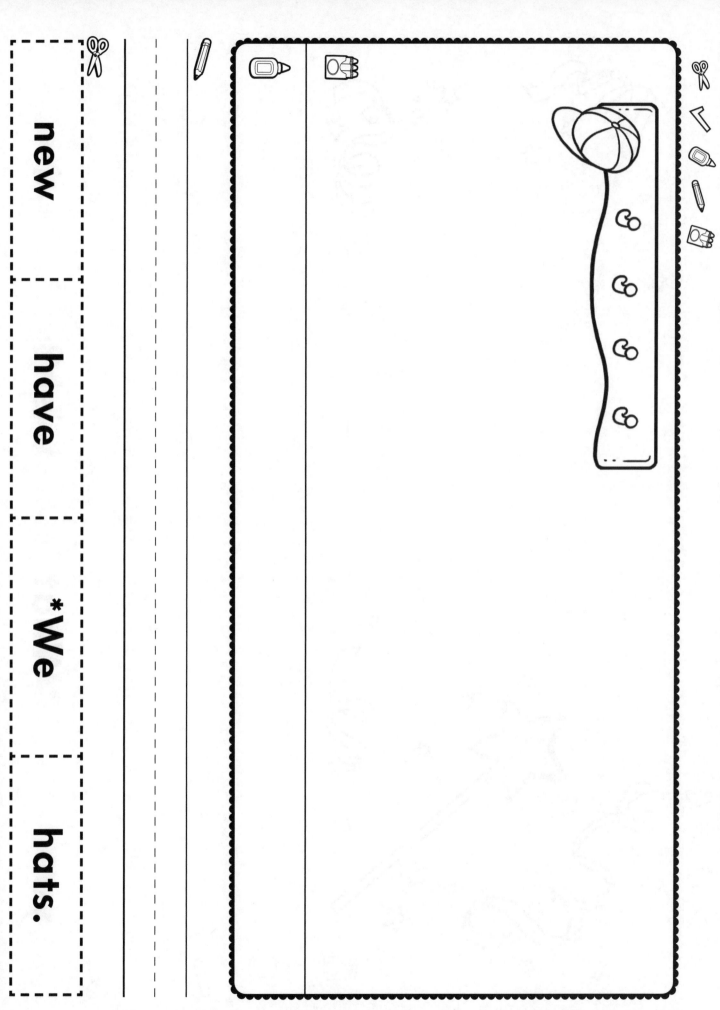

new    have    *We    hats.

*What is your wish?

Cut & Paste Sight Word Sentences • Gr. K–1 © 2012 Creative Teaching Press

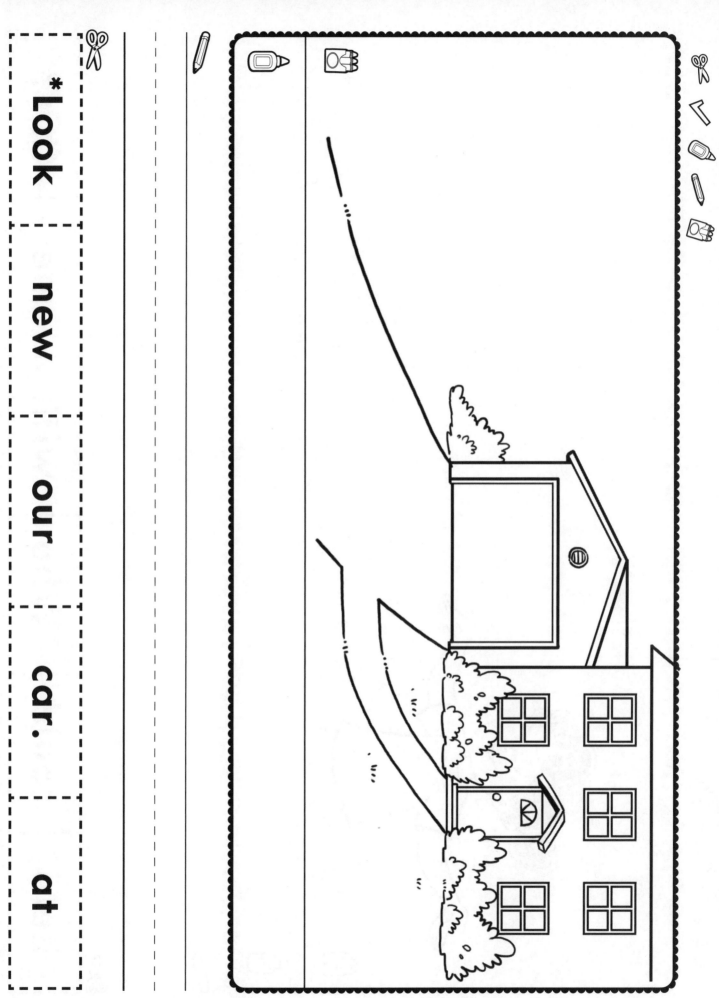

*Look | new | our | car. | at

Cut & Paste Sight Word Sentences • Gr. K–1 © 2012 Creative Teaching Press

help | could | *Who | with | me | this?

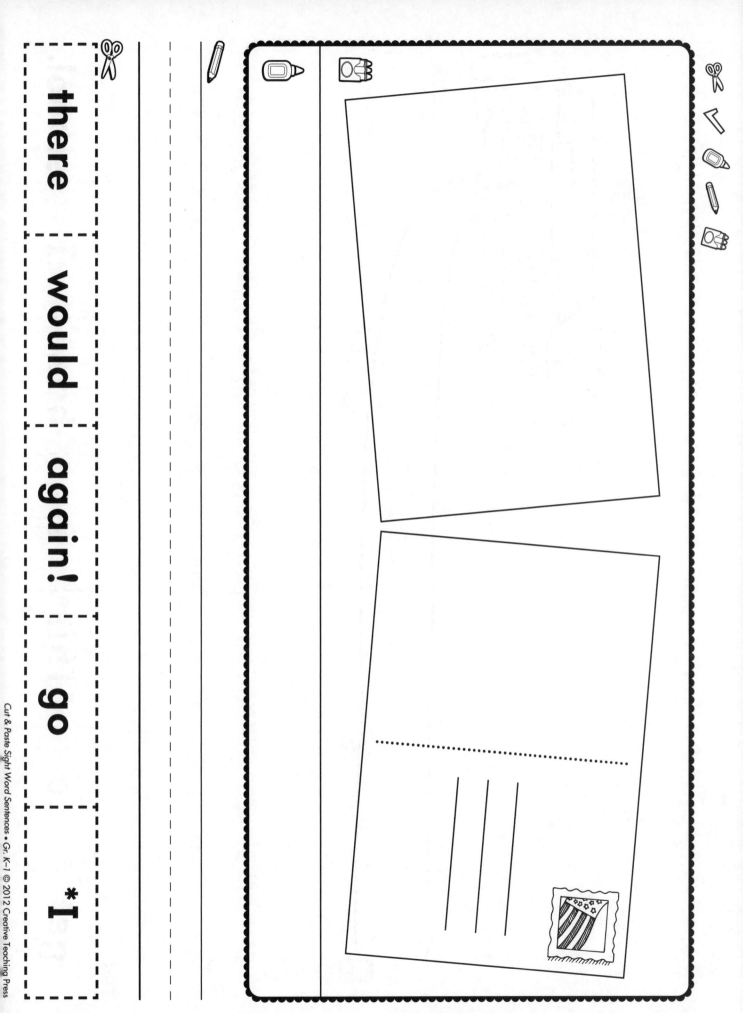

there | would | again! | go | \*I

Cut & Paste Sight Word Sentences • Gr. K–1 © 2012 Creative Teaching Press

get | to | *This | is | how | I | school.

Cut & Paste Sight Word Sentences • Gr. K–1 © 2012 Creative Teaching Press

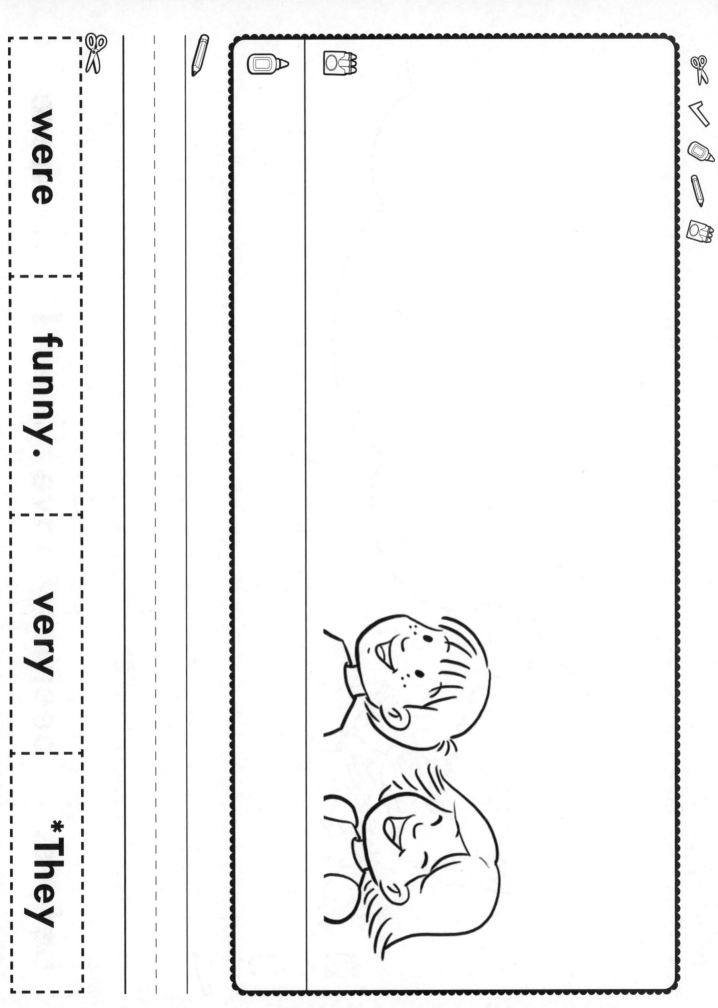

were | funny. | very | *They

here

*I

have

been

before.

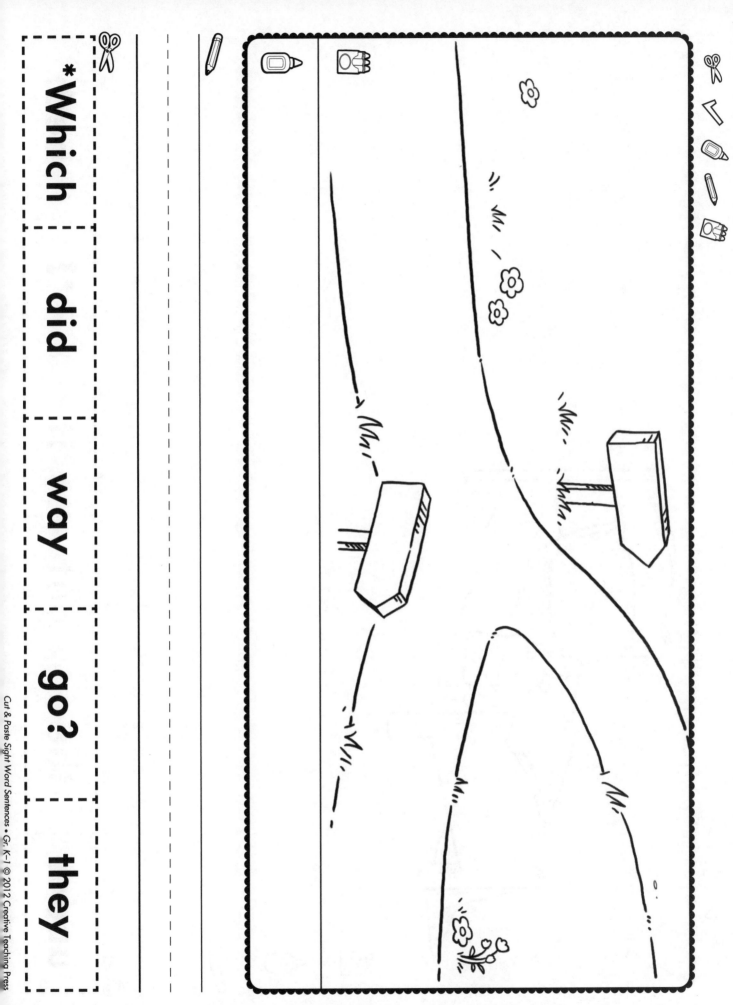

*Which did way go? they

Cut & Paste Sight Word Sentences • Gr. K–1 © 2012 Creative Teaching Press

under the put it *I bed.

Cut & Paste Sight Word Sentences • Gr. K–1 © 2012 Creative Teaching Press

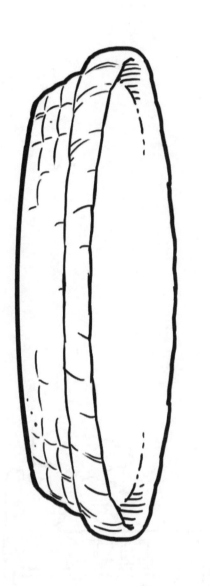

*Who | a | could | home? | them | give

cats | outside | house. | the | *Two | were

Cut & Paste Sight Word Sentences • Gr. K–1 © 2012 Creative Teaching Press

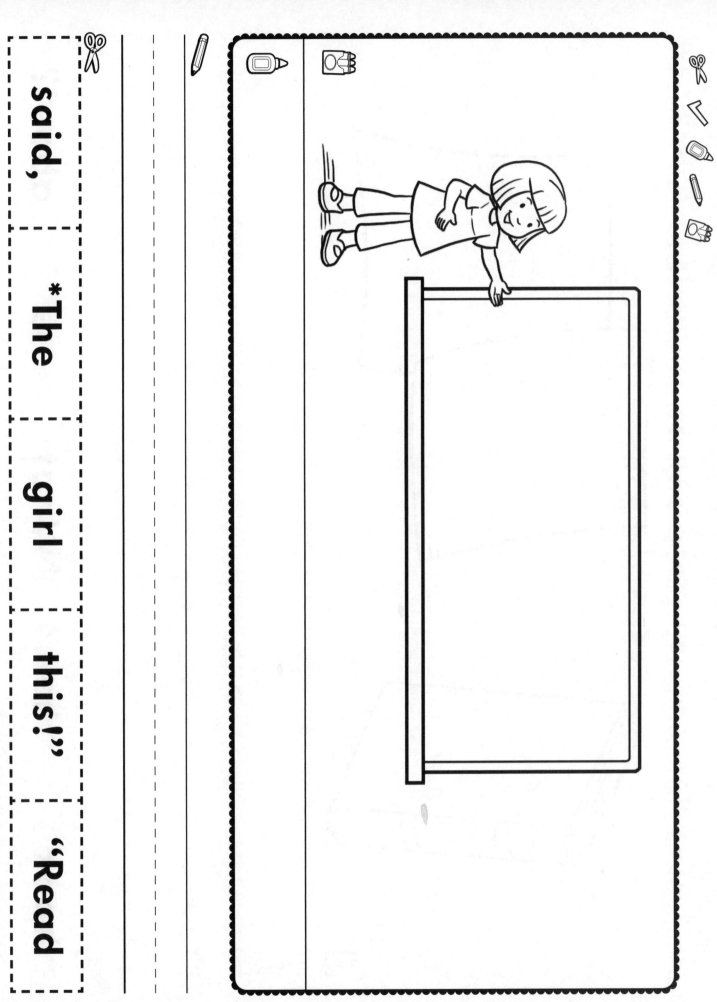

said,    "The    girl    this!"    "Read

book          the          *What          is          about?

Cut & Paste Sight Word Sentences • Gr. K–1 © 2012 Creative Teaching Press

# Sight Word Phrases

| | | |
|---|---|---|
| ☐ I like | ☐ here is | ☐ she saw |
| ☐ do this | ☐ here is my | ☐ I know |
| ☐ you can | ☐ will you get | ☐ I know how |
| ☐ you can have | ☐ for me | ☐ how to |
| ☐ can see it | ☐ go with us | ☐ do not |
| ☐ we have | ☐ these are | ☐ with this |
| ☐ he had | ☐ we will | ☐ with that |
| ☐ we are at | ☐ that makes | ☐ this is how |
| ☐ come see | ☐ for him | ☐ I get |
| ☐ come back | ☐ just one | ☐ who will |
| ☐ that is | ☐ which one | ☐ who was here |
| ☐ look at | ☐ very good | ☐ help me |
| ☐ what is in | ☐ she has | ☐ they could |
| ☐ I will be | ☐ she has many | ☐ he would |
| ☐ it is on | ☐ the boy said | ☐ go there |

| |
|---|
| ☐ find me |
| ☐ they were |
| ☐ I have been |
| ☐ which way |
| ☐ did they go |
| ☐ your friend |
| ☐ by the tree |
| ☐ the girl said |
| ☐ read this |
| ☐ this is about |
| ☐ what is this |
| ☐ there is |
| ☐ there are |
| ☐ our school |
| ☐ the girl |

| *I | like | this. |
|----|------|-------|

| *We | like | to | do | this. |
|-----|------|-----|-----|-------|

| *I | can | see | it. |
|----|-----|-----|-----|

| *It | is | on | the | wall. |
|-----|----|----|-----|-------|

| *You | can | have | this. |
|------|-----|------|-------|

| *Can | you | find | me? |
|------|-----|------|-----|

| *It | is | by | the | tree. |
|-----|----|----|-----|-------|

| *We | are | at | school. |
|-----|-----|----|---------|

| *Come | see | my | bugs. |
|-------|-----|----|-------|

| *Come | back | here! |
|-------|------|-------|

Cut & Paste Sight Word Sentences • Gr. K–1 © 2012 Creative Teaching Press

| *That | is | big | and | red. |
|---|---|---|---|---|

| *Who | was | here? |
|---|---|---|

| *We | will | have | a | picnic. |
|---|---|---|---|---|

| *Here | is | my | friend. |
|---|---|---|---|

| *What | can | I | be? |
|---|---|---|---|

| *What | will | this | be? |
|---|---|---|---|

| *What | is | in | the | box? |
|---|---|---|---|---|

| *His | dog | can | run | here. |
|---|---|---|---|---|

| *We | like | to | play | here. |
|---|---|---|---|---|

| *You | can | go | with | us. |
|---|---|---|---|---|

*She saw it and ran.

*We will all eat here.

*That makes her so happy!

*Will you get it for him?

*You can take just one.

*Which one is yours?

*Here is their good work.

*Will you get this for me?

*She has many little toys.

*The boy said, "Put that down!"

*He had a lot of fun.

*These are from me to you.

*I know how to do that.

*Do not play with that!

*Look what they found!

*I want to sleep there.

*We have new hats.

*What is your wish?

*Look at our new car.

*Who could help me with this?

Cut & Paste Sight Word Sentences • Gr. K–1 © 2012 Creative Teaching Press

*I would go there again!

*This is how I get to school.

*They were very funny.

*I have been here before.

*Which way did they go?

*I put it under the bed.

*Who could give them a home?

*Two cats were outside the house.

*The girl said, "Read this!"

*What is the book about?